THE
AUDUBON
BIRDS
COLOURING BOOK

ARCTURUS

ARCTURUS

This edition published in 2017 by Arcturus Publishing Limited
26/27 Bickels Yard, 151–153 Bermondsey Street,
London SE1 3HA

Copyright © Arcturus Holdings Limited

ISBN: 978-1-78428-589-0
CH005426NT
Supplier 29, Date 1216, Print Run 5917

Printed in China

Introduction

Birds have always fascinated us, with their ability to fly, their uplifting song and their varied plumage. Recording them on paper is notoriously difficult as they are never at rest for long, but throughout history artists have endeavoured to create accurate depictions of birds that do justice to their beauty.

In this colouring book you will find a selection of more than forty artworks from *Birds of America*, the masterpiece of John James Audubon (1785–1851) and perhaps the greatest work of ornithology ever made. In 1820, Audubon set off into the North American wilderness with just one young assistant, intending to create the most complete record of bird species to date. He shot the majority of bird specimens he identified, wiring them into lifelike positions before painting them. While Audubon's methods would not be acceptable today, the public and the scientific community would be forever indebted for the masterwork that he produced. The 435 life-size prints that appear in the final edition of *Birds of America* are astonishing works of art, both accurate and full of interest. The birds are remarkably lifelike, set against plants that they would choose in the wild.

In this collection you can find some of the best known birds of North America, including the jewel-like blue jay, encountered from Florida in the south to Alberta and Saskatchewan in the north; the golden eagle, a magnificent predator revered by Native American tribes, and the cheery house finch, a familiar sight at bird feeders from coast to coast.

While many of the birds in these pages are a familiar sight in North America today, a few of the species recorded by Audubon are now extinct, including two that feature here: the passenger pigeon and the Carolina parakeet. They serve as a reminder that bird populations can be vulnerable to human activity, and of the need for conservation.

Opposite each of the original illustrations is a rendition in black line ready for colouring. The birds' plumage is often finely detailed with subtle variations in tone, but if you choose your colours carefully and take your time, you will be rewarded with a precise depiction of each species. A full set of coloured pencils will produce excellent results, as will watercolour pencils to which you can add water to obtain a smooth wash of colour (limit the amount of water you use to avoid the paper buckling). Whichever method you choose, you can enjoy following in Audubon's footsteps, paying homage to the beauty of North America's birds.

Key: List of plates

1 Bay-breasted warbler
(Setophaga castanea)

2 Great gray owl
(Strix nebulosa)

3 Connecticut warbler
(Oporornis agilis)

4 American flamingo
(Phoenicopterus ruber)

5 Baltimore oriole
(Icterus galbula)

6 Rough-legged hawk
(Buteo lagopus)

7 Eastern bluebird
(Sialia sialis)

8 Carolina wren
(Thryothorus ludovicianus)

9 Carolina parrot or
parakeet
(Conuropsis carolinensis) *

10 Black-throated blue
warbler
(Setophaga caerulescens)

11 Green-breasted
mango hummingbird
(Anthrocothorax prevostii)

12 Red-shouldered hawk
(Buteo lineatus)

13 Cerulean warbler
(Setophaga cerulea)

14 Fork-tailed flycatcher
(Tyrannus savana)

15 Painted bunting
(Passerina ciris)

16 Belted kingfisher
(Megaceryle alcyon)

17 Chestnut-backed
chickadee
(Poecile rufescens)

18 Great blue heron
(Ardea Herodias)

19 Yellow-throated warbler
(Setophaga dominica)

20 Passenger pigeon
(Ectopistes migratorius) *

21 Violet-green swallow
(Tachycineta thalassina)

22 American redstart
(Setophaga ruticilla)

23 Barred owl
(Strix varia)

24 Blue jay
(Cyanocitta cristata)

25 Pelagic cormorant
(Phalacrocorax pelagicus)

26 Red-breasted sapsucker
(Sphyrapicus ruber)

27 Summer tanager
(Piranga rubra)

28 Bell's vireo
(Vireo bellii)

29 Golden eagle
(Aquila chrysaetos)

30 Blue-gray gnatcatcher
(Polioptila caerulea)

31 Western tanager
(Piranga ludoviciana)

32 House finch
(Haemorhous mexicanus)

33 Blue grosbeak
(Passerina caerulea)

34 Dickcissel
(Spiza americana)

35 Yellow-billed magpie
(Pica nuttalli)

36 American avocet
(Recurvirostra americana)

37 Northern shoveler
(Anas clypeata)

38 Roseate spoonbill
(Platalea ajaja)

39 Mountain quail
(Oreortyx pictus)

40 Red-throated loon
(Gavia stellata)

41 Northern fulmar
(Fulmarus glacialis)

42 Horned puffin
(Fratercula corniculata)

43 Brown pelican
(Pelecanus occidentalis)

44 Blue-winged teal
(Anas discors)

Setophaga castanea

Bay-breasted warbler

Strix nebulosa

Great gray owl

Oporornis agilis

Connecticut warbler

Phoenicopterus ruber

American flamingo

Baltimore oriole

Icterus galbula

Buteo lagopus

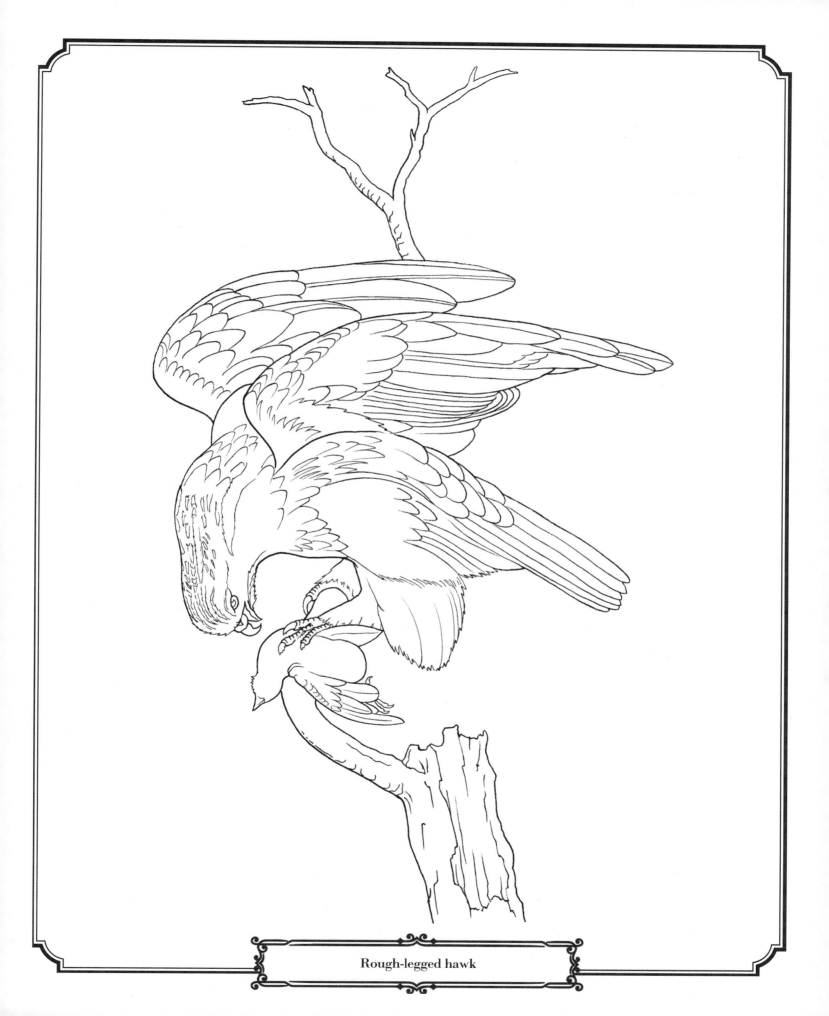

Rough-legged hawk

Sialia sialis

Eastern bluebird

Thryothorus ludovicianus

Carolina wren

Conuropsis carolinensis

Carolina parrot or parakeet

Setophaga caerulescens

Black-throated blue warbler

Anthrocothorax prevostii

Green-breasted mango hummingbird

Buteo lineatus

Red-shouldered hawk

Setophaga cerulea

Cerulean warbler

Tyrannus savana

Fork-tailed flycatcher

Passerina ciris

Painted bunting

Megaceryle alcyon

Belted kingfisher

Poecile rufescens

Chestnut-backed chickadee

Ardea Herodias

Great blue heron

Setophaga dominica

Yellow-throated warbler

Ectopistes migratorius

Passenger pigeon

Tachycineta thalassina

Violet-green swallow

Setophaga ruticilla

American redstart

Strix varia

Barred owl

Cyanocitta cristata

Blue jay

Phalacrocorax pelagicus

Pelagic cormorant

Sphyrapicus ruber

Red-breasted sapsucker

Piranga rubra

Summer tanager

Vireo bellii

Bell's vireo

Aquila chrysaetos

Golden eagle

Polioptila caerulea

Blue-gray gnatcatcher

Piranga ludoviciana

Western tanager

Haemorhous mexicanus

House finch

Passerina caerulea

Blue grosbeak

Spiza americana

Dickcissel

Pica nuttalli

Yellow-billed magpie

Recurvirostra americana

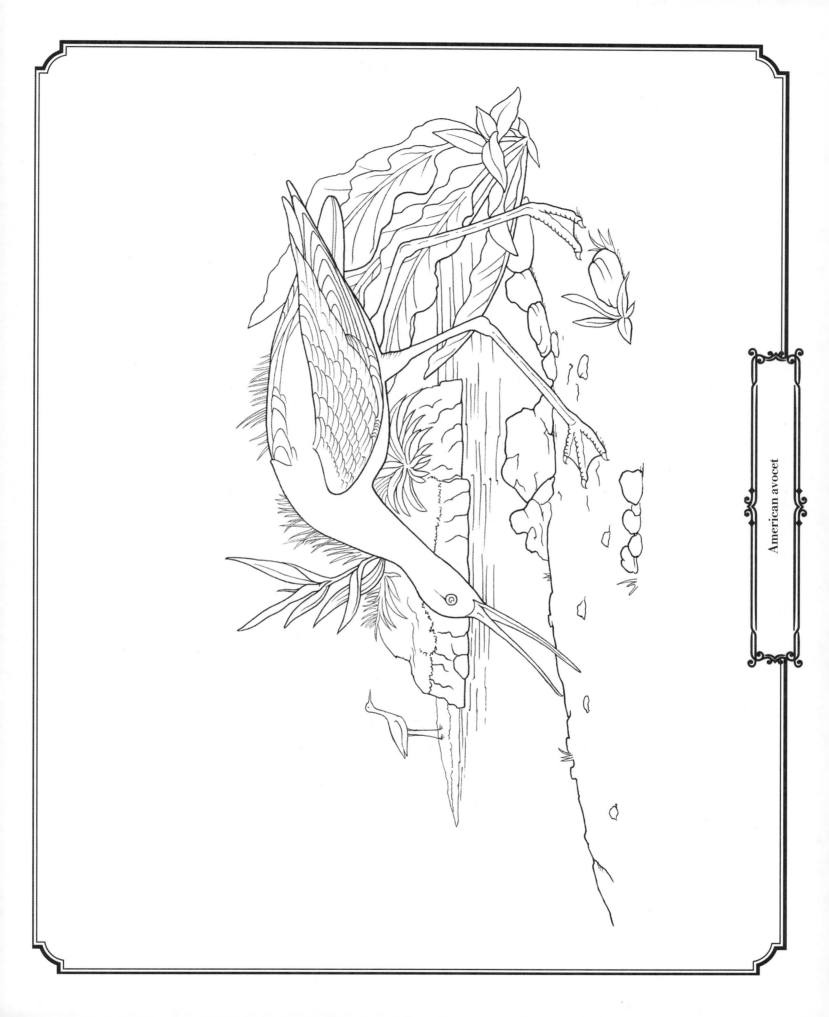

American avocet

Anas clypeata

Northern shoveler

Platalea ajaja

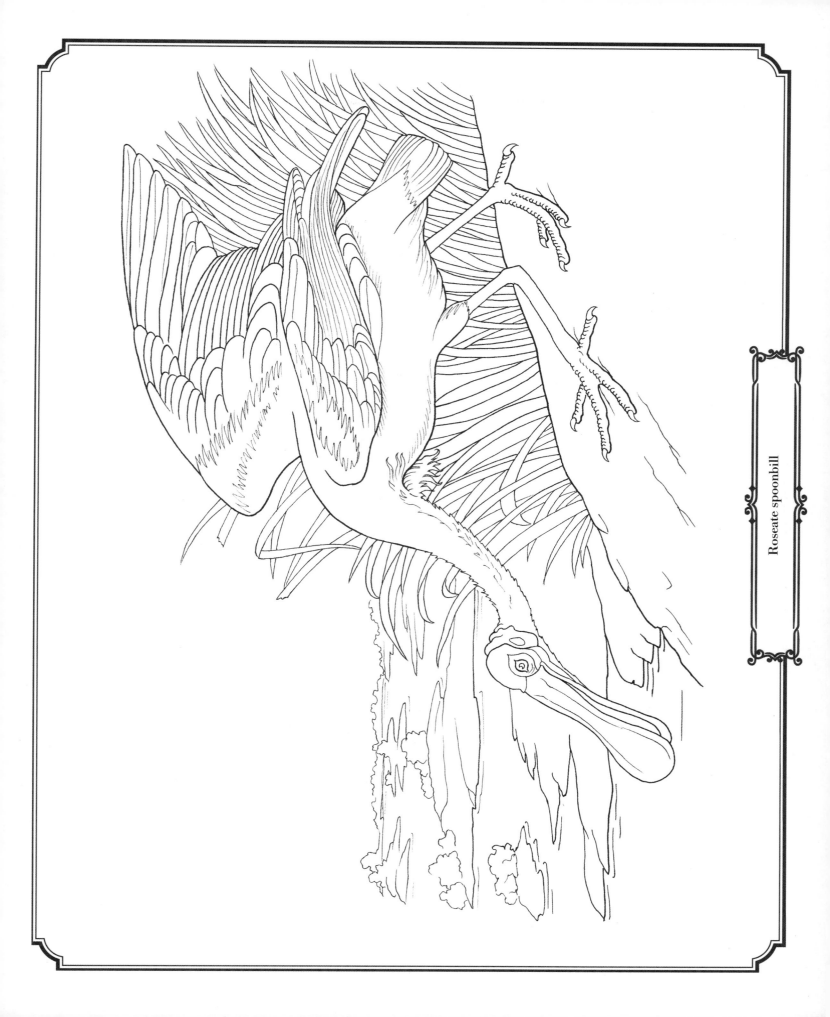

Roseate spoonbill

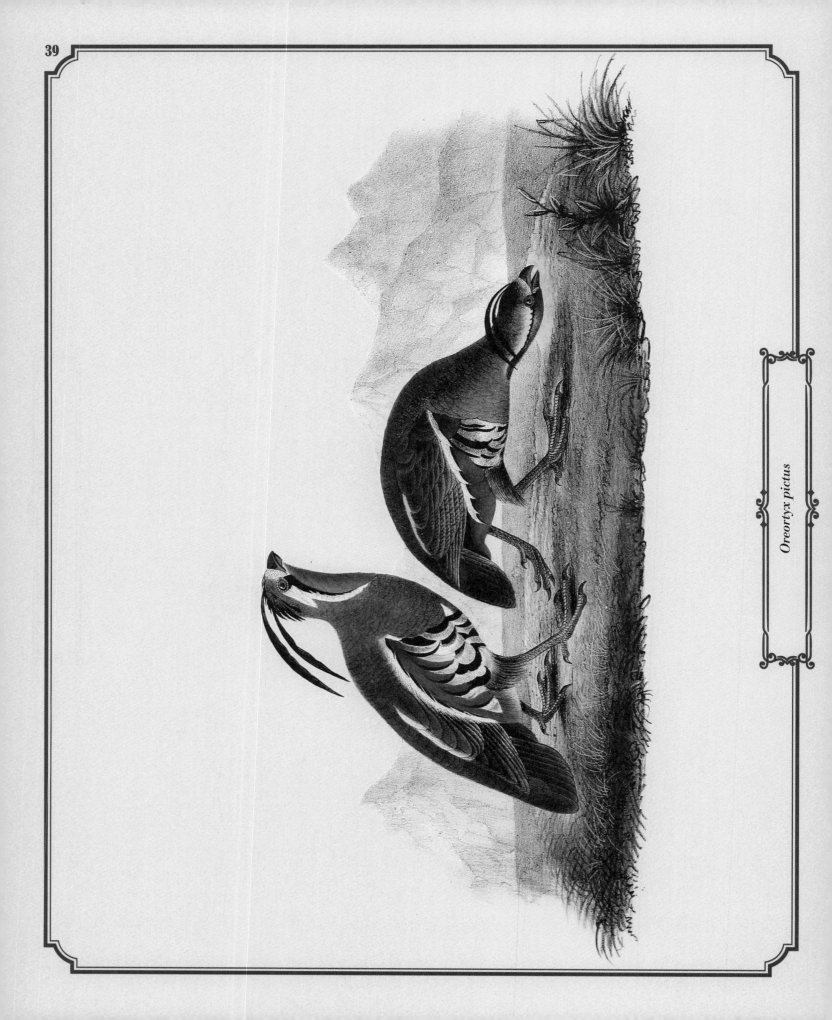

Oreortyx pictus

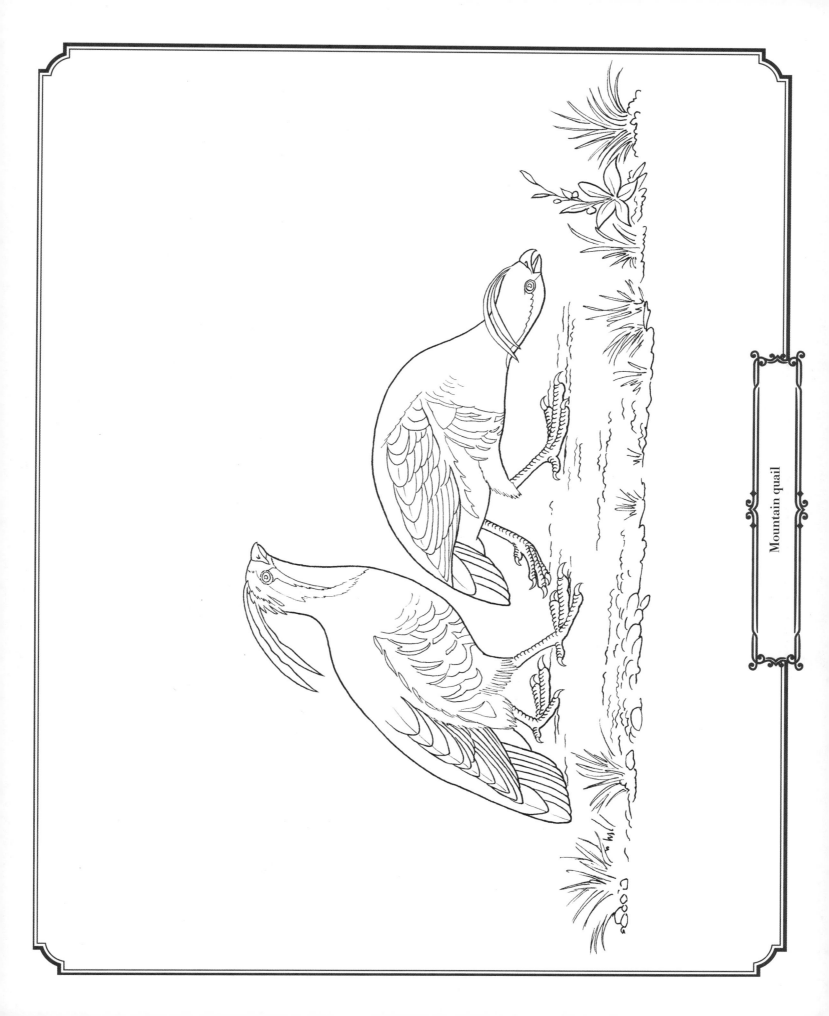

Mountain quail

40

Gavia stellata

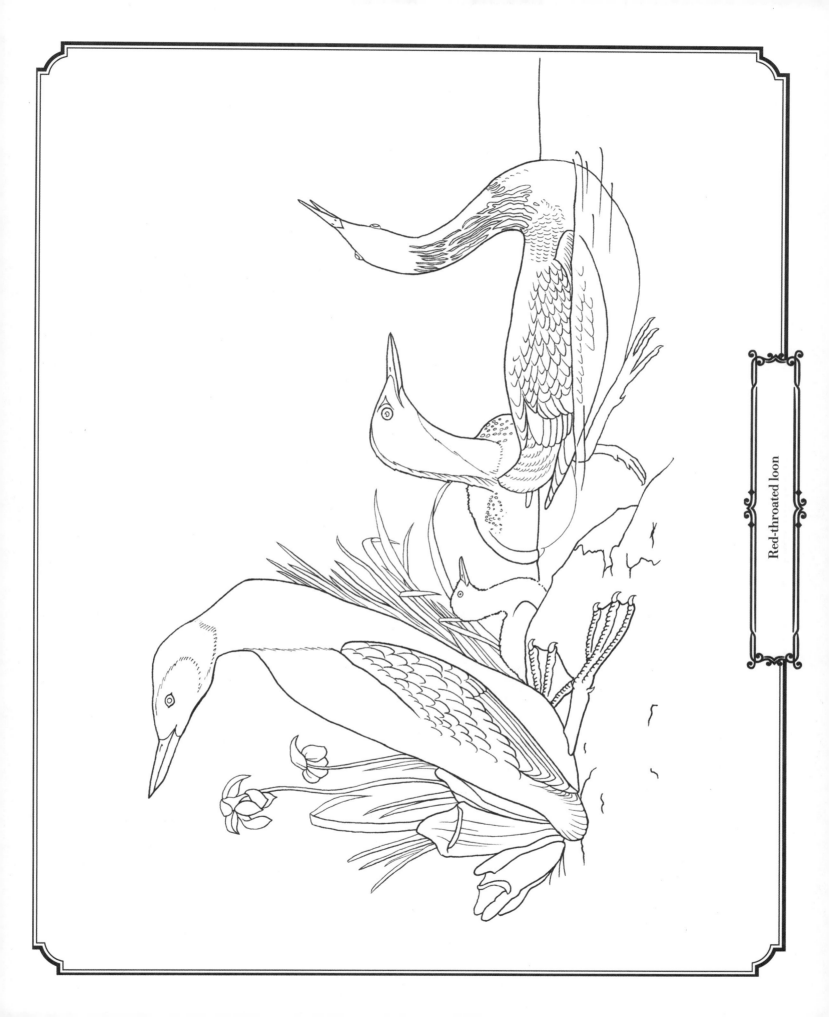

Red-throated loon

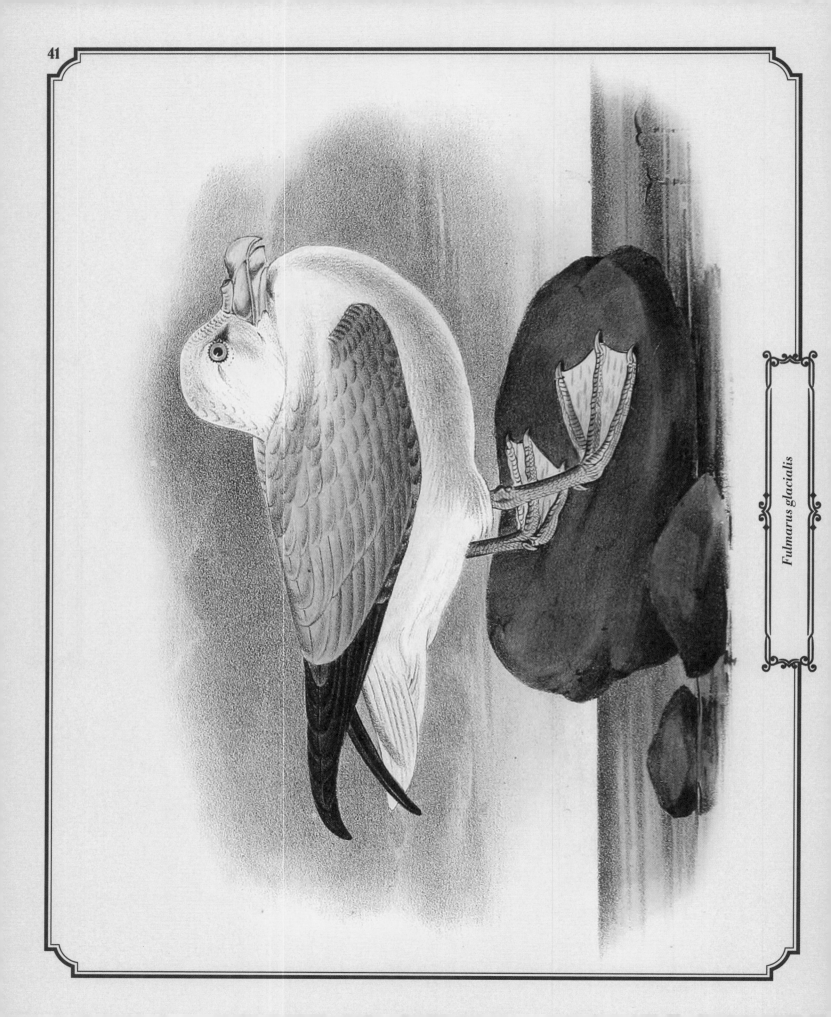

Fulmarus glacialis

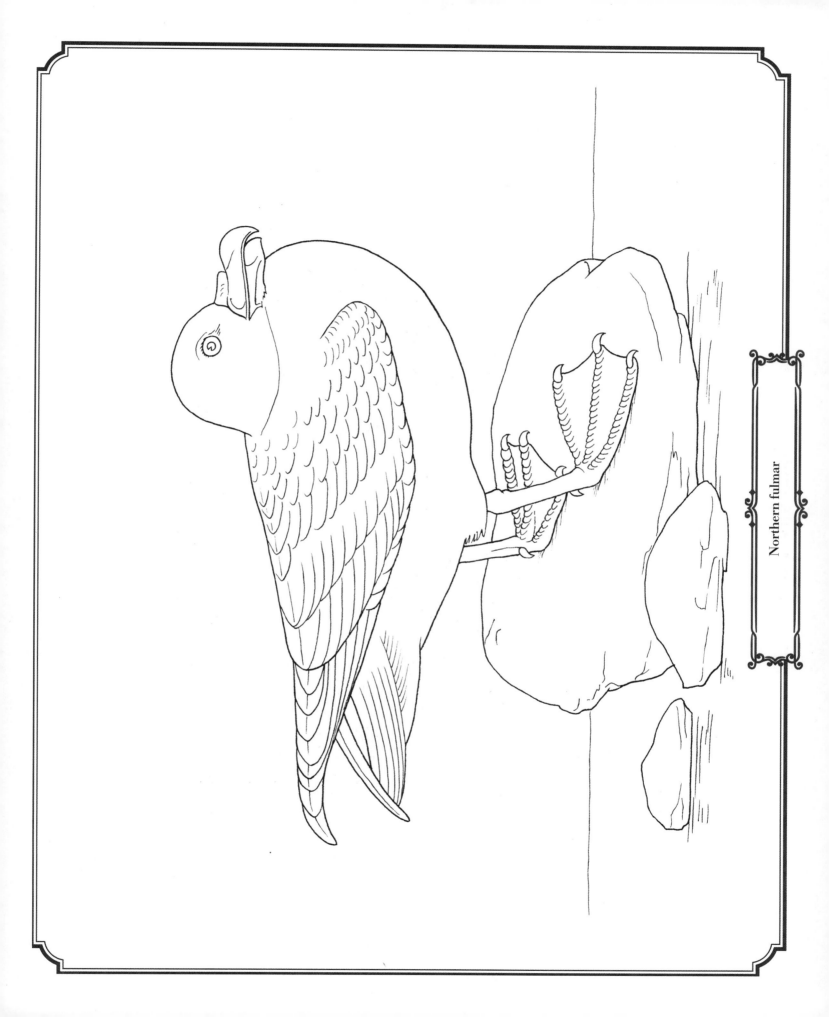

Northern fulmar

Fratercula corniculata

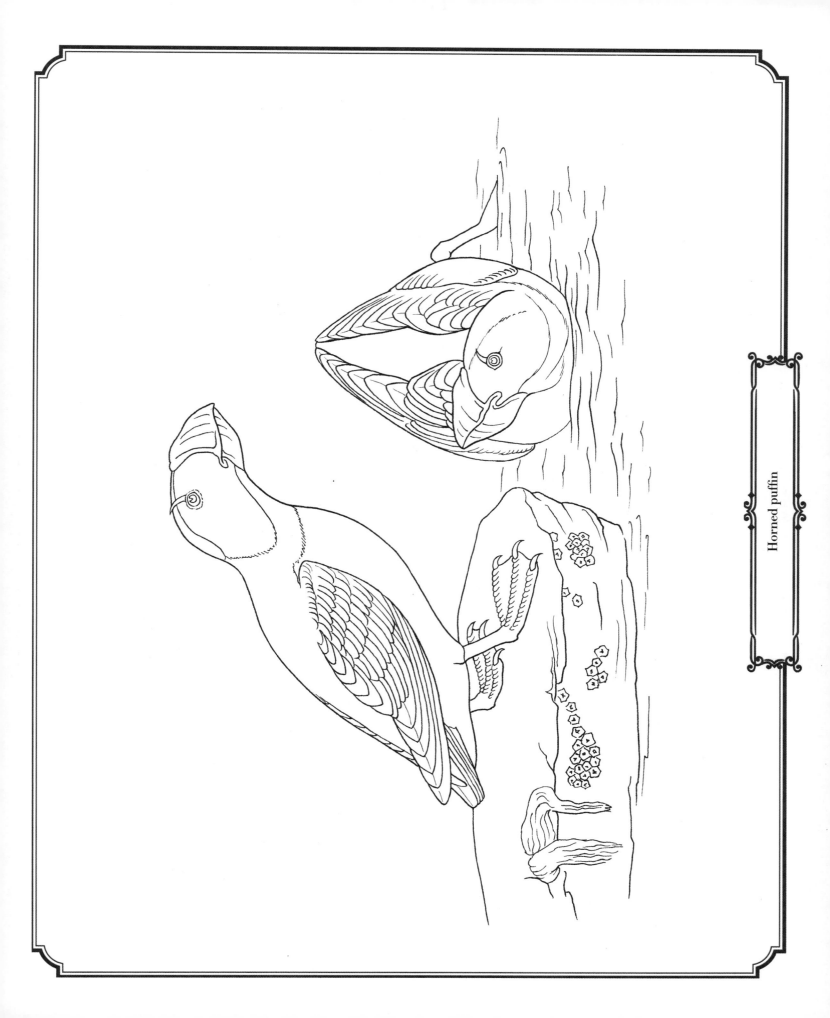

Horned puffin

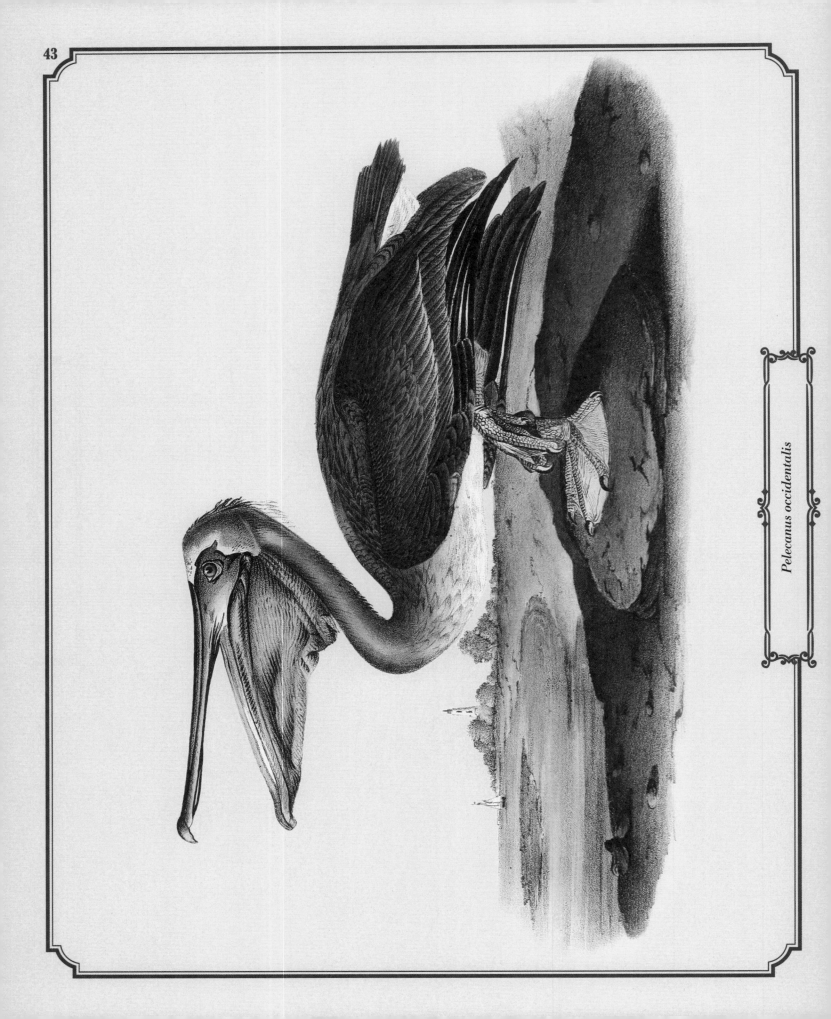

Pelecanus occidentalis

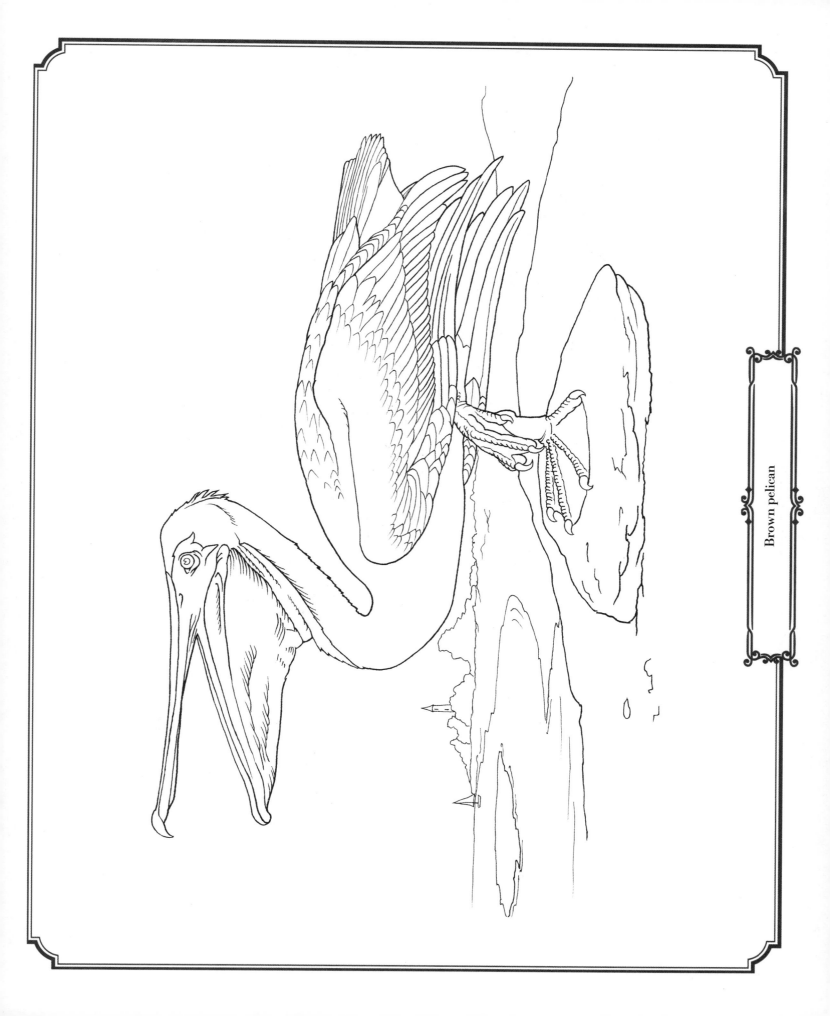

Brown pelican

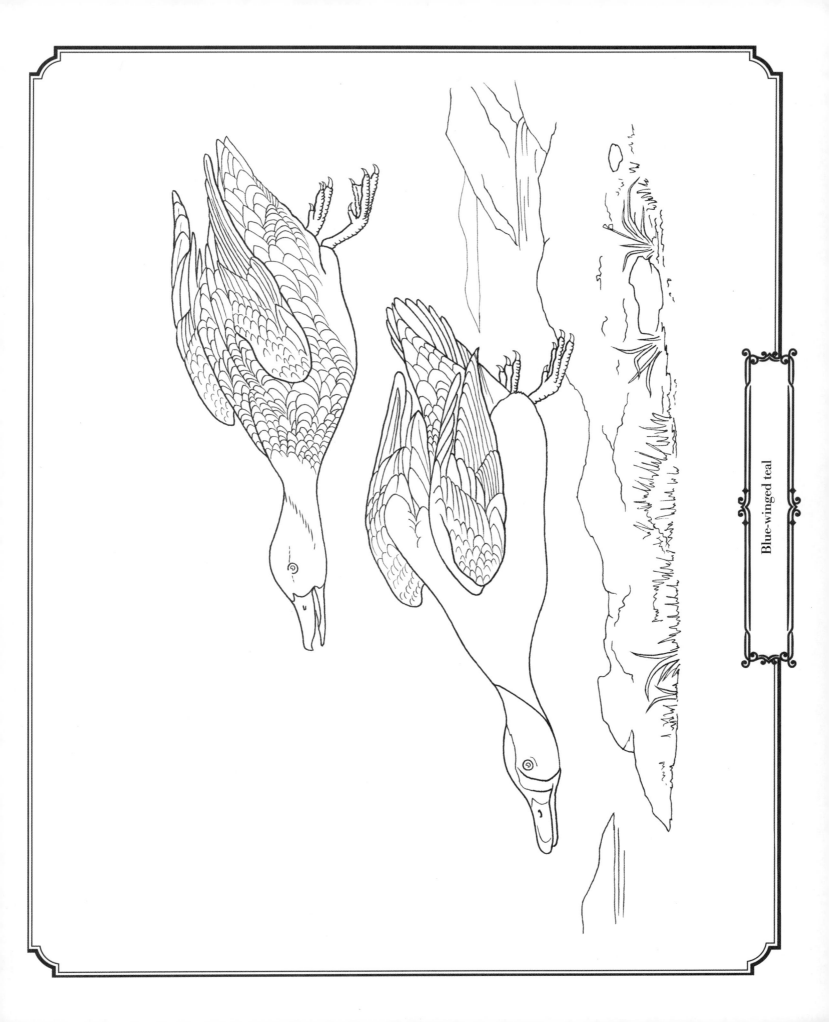

Blue-winged teal